Volume Nine

MY NINTH CLASSIC COLLECTION
CONTAINS:

A GIFT FOR YOU

GREAT IMPRESSIONS

PICK OF THE BUNCH

JiM DAViS

RR

First published by Ravette Publishing 2002

Printed and bound in Great Britain
for Ravette Publishing Limited,
Unit 3, Tristar Centre,
Star Road, Partridge Green,
West Sussex RH13 8RA

by Cox & Wyman Ltd, Reading, Berkshire

ISBN: 1 84161 149 2

Garfield

A Gift For You

JIM DAVIS

RR

© 1991 United Feature Syndicate, Inc.

JIM DAVIS 1-15

JIM DAVIS 1-17

© 1991 United Feature Syndicate, inc.

© 1991 United Feature Syndicate Inc

© 1991 United Feature Syndicate, Inc.

© 1991 United Feature Syndicate, Inc.

BONNNNG!

© 1991 United Feature Syndicate, Inc.

I SUPPOSE **YOU** CAN FIX BETTER PANCAKES!

JIM DAVIS 2-8

© 1991 United Feature Syndicate, Inc.

LOOK OUT, WORLD! HERE I COME!

© 1991 United Feature Syndicate, Inc.

I'M BETTING ON THE WORLD

JIM DAVIS 2-28

© 1991 United Feature Syndicate, Inc.

© 1991 United Feature Syndicate, Inc.

JIM DAVIS 4-15

© 1991 United Feature Syndicate, Inc.

UH... GARFIELD...

BECAUSE NAP ATTACKS CAN STRIKE ANYTIME, ANYWHERE, WITHOUT WARNING, THAT'S WHY

JIM DAVIS 4-16

JIM DAVIS 4-19

WHAT MICE?

RIP RIP
RIP RIP RIP
RIP RIP RIP

© 1991 United Feature Syndicate, Inc.

NOW THAT WE'RE DONE READING
OUR NEWSPAPER, MAYBE WE
CAN SCRATCH OUR TUMMY

JIM DAVIS 5-9

GARFIELD... WHAT BROKEN LAMP?

JIM DAVIS 5-10

© 1991 United Feature Syndicate, Inc.

JIM DAVIS 5-22

GOOSH!

© 1991 United Feature Syndicate, Inc.

FROM NOW ON, LET'S BE PUTTING WATER IN THE WATER DISH, AND FOOD IN THE FOOD DISH, OKAY?

© 1991 United Feature Syndicate, Inc.

JIM DAVIS 5-25

NO FAIR!

© 1991 United Feature Syndicate, Inc.

YOU GOT A HEAD START ON THE GOOFING OFF!

© 1991 United Feature Syndicate, Inc.

Garfield
Great
Impressions

JiM DAViS

© 1991 United Feature Syndicate, Inc.

JIM DAVIS 6-18

© 1991 United Feature Syndicate, Inc.

I HATE IT WHEN I CAN'T SEE MY FEET

© 1991 United Feature Syndicate, Inc.

I COULD BE WEARING WEIRD SHOES AND NOT KNOW IT

JIM DAVIS 6-28

© 1991 United Feature Syndicate, Inc.

FISSSS
ZIT ZIT ZIT ZIT
FISSSS
ZIT ZIT ZIT ZIT

© 1991 United Feature Syndicate, inc.

© 1991 United Feature Syndicate, Inc.

JIM DAVIS 7-18

© 1991 United Feature Syndicate, Inc.

7-20   JIM DAVIS

CLICK-
CHUNK

© 1991 United Feature Syndicate, Inc.

JiM DAViS 7-30

© 1991 United Feature Syndicate, Inc.

© 1991 United Feature Syndicate, Inc

© 1991 United Feature Syndicate, Inc.

JIM DAVIS 9-26

© 1991 United Feature Syndicate, Inc.

JIM DAVIS 10-21

© 1991 United Feature Syndicate, Inc.

JiM DAViS 10-25

Garfield

Pick Of The Bunch

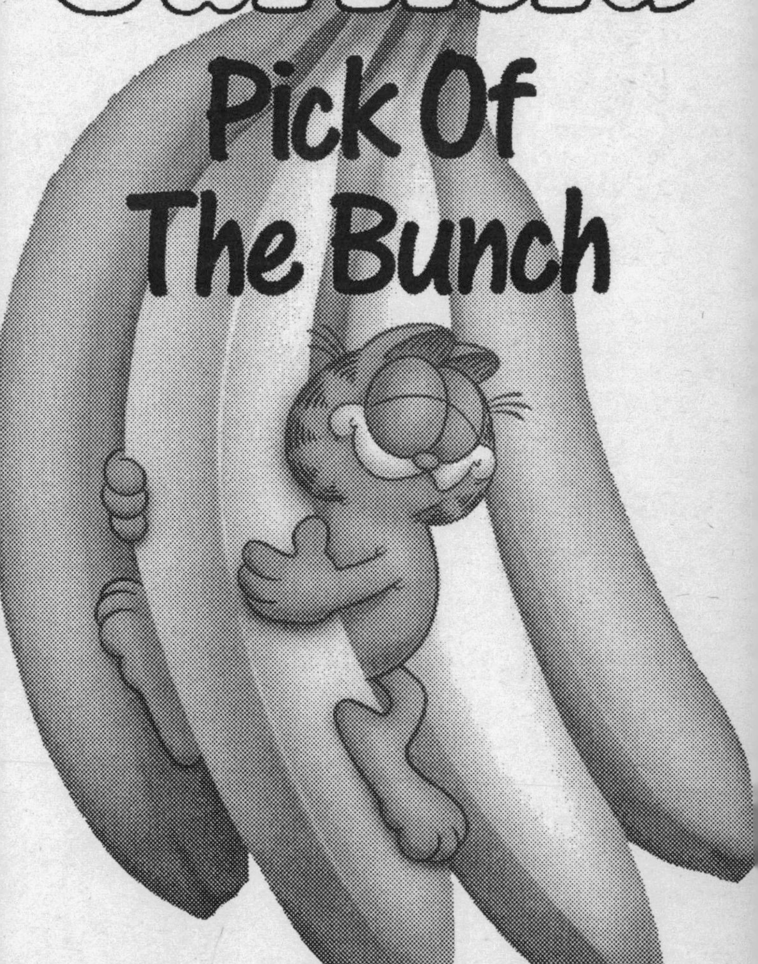

JIM DAVIS

RR

1

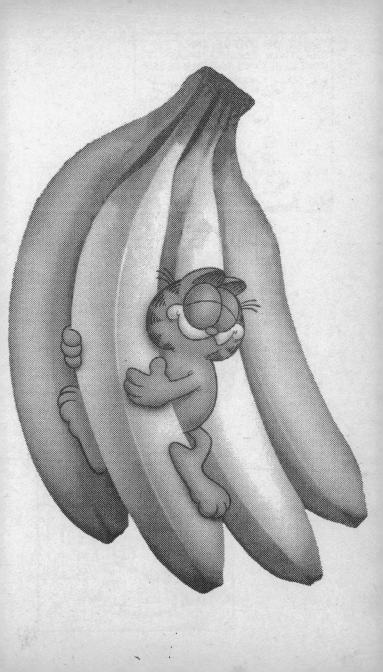

© 1991 United Feature Syndicate, Inc.

JIM DAVIS 11-1

© 1991 United Feature Syndicate, Inc.

JIM DAVIS 11-2

© 1991 United Feature Syndicate, Inc.

© 1991 United Feature Syndicate, Inc.

JIM DAVIS 11-13

© 1991 United Feature Syndicate, Inc.

© 1991 United Feature Syndicate, inc.

© 1991 United Feature Syndicate, Inc.

BEWARE OF DOG

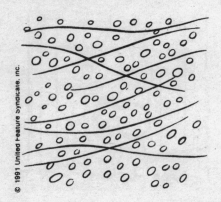

FINALLY... A NICE, PEACEFUL MEAL

© 1992 United Feature Syndicate, Inc.

CRUNCH!

HAVE YOU SEEN MY LUCKY ROCK?

© 1992 United Feature Syndicate, Inc.

© 1992 United Feature Syndicate, Inc.

© 1992 United Feature Syndicate, Inc.

© 1992 United Feature Syndicate, Inc.

JIM DAVIS 2-10

© 1992 United Feature Syndicate, Inc.

© 1992 United Feature Syndicate, Inc.

JIM DAVIS 2-26

I WONDER IF OTHER PEOPLE'S PETS HAVE WILD MOOD SWINGS?

GRRRR   GRRRR

© 1992 United Feature Syndicate, Inc.

OTHER GARFIELD BOOKS AVAILABLE

Pocket Books	Price	ISBN
Bon Appetit	£3.50	1 84161 038 0
Byte Me	£3.50	1 84161 009 7
Double Trouble	£3.50	1 84161 008 9
Eat My Dust	£3.50	1 84161 098 4
Fun in the Sun	£3.50	1 84161 097 6
The Gladiator	£3.50	1 85304 941 7
Gooooooal!	£3.50	1 84161 037 2
Great Impressions	£3.50	1 85304 191 2
Hangs On	£2.99	1 85304 784 8
In Training	£3.50	1 85304 785 6
The Irresistible	£3.50	1 85304 940 9
Let's Party	£3.50	1 85304 906 9
Light Of My Life	£3.50	1 85304 353 2
On The Right Track	£3.50	1 85304 907 7
Pick Of The Bunch	£2.99	1 85304 258 7
Says It With Flowers	£2.99	1 85304 316 8
Shove At First Sight	£3.50	1 85304 990 5
To Eat, Or Not To Eat?	£3.50	1 85304 991 3
Wave Rebel	£3.50	1 85304 317 6
With Love From Me To You	£3.50	1 85304 392 3

new titles available February 2003

	Price	ISBN
No. 45 – Pop Star	£3.50	1 84161 151 4
No. 46 – Below Par	£3.50	1 84161 152 2

Theme Books	Price	ISBN
Guide to Behaving Badly	£4.50	1 85304 892 5
Guide to Cat Napping	£4.50	1 84161 087 9
Guide to Coffee Mornings	£4.50	1 84161 086 0
Guide to Creatures Great & Small	£3.99	1 85304 998 0
Guide to Healthy Living	£3.99	1 85304 972 7
Guide to Insults	£3.99	1 85304 895 X
Guide to Pigging Out	£4.50	1 85304 893 3
Guide to Romance	£3.99	1 85304 894 1
Guide to The Seasons	£3.99	1 85304 999 9
Guide to Successful Living	£3.99	1 85304 973 5

new series now available
2-in-1 Theme Books

	Price	ISBN
The Gruesome Twosome	£6.99	1 84161 143 3
Out For The Couch	£6.99	1 84161 144 1

Classics	Price	ISBN
Volume One	£5.99	1 85304 970 0
Volume Two	£5.99	1 85304 971 9
Volume Three	£5.99	1 85304 996 4
Volume Four	£5.99	1 85304 997 2
Volume Five	£5.99	1 84161 022 4
Volume Six	£5.99	1 84161 023 2
Volume Seven	£5.99	1 84161 088 7
Volume Eight	£5.99	1 84161 089 5

new title now available

Volume Ten	£5.99	1 84161 150 6

new series now available

Little Books		
Food 'n' Fitness	£2.50	1 84161 145 X
Laughs	£2.50	1 84161 146 8
Love 'n' Stuff	£2.50	1 84161 147 6
Wit 'n' Wisdom	£2.50	1 84161 148 4

Miscellaneous

new title available September 2002

Treasury 3	£9.99	1 84161 142 5
Treasury 2	£9.99	1 84161 042 9
Address Book (indexed) inc vat	£4.99	1 85304 904 2
21st Birthday Celebration Book	£9.99	1 85304 995 6

All Garfield books are available at your local bookshop or from the publisher at the address below. Just tick the titles required and send the form with your payment to:-

RAVETTE PUBLISHING
Unit 3, Tristar Centre, Star Road, Partridge Green, West Sussex RH13 8RA

Prices and availability are subject to change without notice.
Please enclose a cheque or postal order made payable to **Ravette Publishing** to the value of the cover price of the book and allow the following for UK postage and packing:

60p for the first book + 30p for each additional book
except *Garfield Treasuries* and *21st Birthday Celebration Book* . . . when please add £3.00 per copy for p&p

Name ....

Address ....

....

....